THE MOST MEMORABLE VOCAL DUETS OF ALL TIME

DYNAMIC DUOS

THE BEST DUETS EVER!

WISE PUBLICATIONS
part of The Music Sales Group
LONDON / NEW YORK / PARIS / SYDNEY / COPENHAGEN / BERLIN / MADRID / TOKYO

PUBLISHED BY
WISE PUBLICATIONS
8/9 FRITH STREET, LONDON W1D 3JB, UK.

EXCLUSIVE DISTRIBUTORS:
MUSIC SALES LIMITED
DISTRIBUTION CENTRE, NEWMARKET ROAD,
BURY ST EDMUNDS, SUFFOLK IP33 3YB, UK.
MUSIC SALES PTY LIMITED
120 ROTHSCHILD AVENUE, ROSEBERY, NSW 2018,
AUSTRALIA.

ORDER NO. AM84302
ISBN 0-7119-2602-6

COVER DESIGN BY MICHAEL BELL DESIGN.
COVER PHOTOGRAPH COURTESY OF LFI.
PRINTED IN THE EU.

BABY, IT'S COLD OUTSIDE
TOM JONES & CERYS MATTHEWS
4

CHANGES
KELLY & OZZY OSBOURNE
10

THE CLOSER I GET TO YOU
LUTHER VANDROSS & BEYONCÉ
16

COME WHAT MAY
NICOLE KIDMAN & EWAN McGREGOR
42

DEAD RINGER FOR LOVE
MEAT LOAF & CHER
20

DON'T KNOW MUCH
LINDA RONSTADT & AARON NEVILLE
30

FAIRYTALE OF NEW YORK
THE POGUES & KIRSTY MacCOLL
36

I KNEW YOU WERE WAITING (FOR ME)
ARETHA FRANKLIN & GEORGE MICHAEL
47

ISLANDS IN THE STREAM
KENNY ROGERS & DOLLY PARTON
52

IT TAKES TWO
MARVIN GAYE & KIM WESTON
57

JE T'AIME... MOI NON PLUS
JANE BIRKIN & SERGE GAINSBOURG
62

KIDS
ROBBIE WILLIAMS & KYLIE MINOGUE
65

KINKY BOOTS
PATRICK MACNEE & HONOR BLACKMAN
72

A LITTLE TIME
THE BEAUTIFUL SOUTH
76

NO MORE TEARS (ENOUGH IS ENOUGH)
BARBRA STREISAND & DONNA SUMMER
81

ON MY OWN
PATTI LaBELLE & MICHAEL McDONALD
90

REUNITED
PEACHES & HERB
94

SENZA UNA DONNA (WITHOUT A WOMAN)
ZUCCHERO & PAUL YOUNG
100

SISTERS ARE DOIN' IT FOR THEMSELVES
EURYTHMICS & ARETHA FRANKLIN
104

SOME VELVET MORNING
NANCY SINATRA & LEE HAZLEWOOD
110

SOMETHIN' STUPID
NANCY SINATRA & FRANK SINATRA
115

SOMETHING'S GOTTEN HOLD OF MY HEART
MARC ALMOND & GENE PITNEY
120

TIME TO SAY GOODBYE (CON TE PARTIRO)
SARAH BRIGHTMAN & ANDREA BOCELLI
127

TO ALL THE GIRLS I'VE LOVED BEFORE
JULIO IGLESIAS & WILLIE NELSON
132

UNDER PRESSURE
QUEEN & DAVID BOWIE
136

UP WHERE WE BELONG
JOE COCKER & JENNIFER WARNES
144

WHEN YOU'RE GONE
BRYAN ADAMS & MELANIE C
156

WHERE THE WILD ROSES GROW
NICK CAVE & KYLIE MINOGUE
148

YOU'RE THE ONE THAT I WANT
JOHN TRAVOLTA & OLIVIA NEWTON-JOHN
152

Baby, It's Cold Outside

Words & Music by Frank Loesser

E♭6
fr6
Fm7
fr8
B♭7
fr6
real-ly can't stay.
I've got to go 'way.
This
(Verse 2 see block lyric)
(Male) 1. But ba-by it's cold out-side!
Oh, ba-by it's cold out-side!
(Verse 2 see block lyric)
B♭m9
E♭7
eve-ning has been so ve-ry nice.
My
Been hop-ing that you'd drop in!
I'll hold your hands, they're just like
A♭6
fr3
A♭m7
fr4
mo-ther will start to wor-ry.
My fath-er will be pac-ing the floor.
So
ice.
Beau-ti-ful, what's your hur-ry?
Lis-ten to that fire-place

E♭6
fr6
Cm
fr8
Fm7
fr8
real - ly I'd __ bet - ter scur - ry. Well may - be just a half a drink more.
roar! Oh beau - ti - ful please don't hur - ry, why don't you
B♭7
fr6
E♭6
fr6
__ The neigh - bours might think, _ Say,
put _ some re - cords on _ while I pour. __ Oh, ba - by it's bad out there. _
Fm7
fr8
B♭7
fr6
Fm7
fr8
B♭7
fr6
E♭6
fr6
what's in this drink? _ I wish I knew how __
There's no cabs __ to be had out there. _ Your eyes

B♭m9
fr6
E♭9
fr5
to break this spell.
I ought
are like star - light.
I'll take your hat, your hair looks swell.
A♭7
fr4
F7sus4
fr8
F7
fr8
to say, "No, no, no sir."
At least there will be, ooh! That I tried,
Mind if I move a lit - tle clos - er?
B♭9sus4
B♭7
E♭6
fr6
Cm7
fr8
To Coda
oh hoo! I real - ly can't stay,
ah, but it's
What's the sense of hurt - ing my pride.
Ba - by don't hold out,
ah but it's

F7
fr8
B♭9
fr6
E♭6
fr6
E♭/B♭
fr6
cold out - - - side.
cold out - - - side.
E/B
fr7
E♭/B♭
fr6
B♭7
fr6
E♭
fr6
Cm7
fr8
Fm7
fr8
B♭6
fr5
D.%. al Coda
2. I

(Female) Verse 2:
I simply must go...
The answer is no...
This welcome has been
So nice and warm.
My sister will be suspicious,
My brother will be there at the door,
My maiden aunt's mind is vicious,
Well, maybe just a cigarette more.
I've got to go home...
Say, lend me a comb...
You've really been grand
But don't you see?
There's bound to be talk tomorrow,
At least there will be plenty implied.
I really can't stay,
Ah, but it's cold outside.

(Male) Verse 2:
Oh, baby it's cold outside!
You know it's cold outside!
I'm lucky that you dropped in,
Look out the window at that storm.
Oh, your lips look delicious,
Like waves upon a tropical shore.
Ooh, your lips are delicious,
Never such a blizzard before.
Oh, baby you would freeze out there,
You know, it's up to your knees out there.
I thrill when you touch my hand,
How can you do this thing to me?
Making my life-long sorrow,
Well, if you caught pneumonia and died...
Get over that old doubt,
Ah, but it's cold outside.

Changes

Words & Music by Ozzy Osbourne, Tony Iommi, Geezer Butler & Bill Ward

C
Dm/C
C
Dm/C
(Male) She is my ba - by,
I love her so,
C
Dm
C
Dm/C
but it's too late now,
I've let her go.
C
C/E
F
Cadd9/E
Dm
(Both) We're go - ing through chan - ges,
F
Cadd9/E
Dm
G
we're go - ing through chan - ges.

F
C
Csus4
C
Csus4
C
3fr
(Female) We shared the
Cadd9
Dm7
years,
we shared each day,
I love you dad - dy
C
Dm/C
C
Dm/C
C
but I've found my way.
(Male) You know the world
is an e - vil place,
Dm/A
C/A
Dm11
C
Dm/G
my ba - by's grown now,
she's found her way.

C
C/E
F
Cadd9/E
Dm7
(Both) We're go - ing through chan - ges,
F
Cadd9/E
Dm7
G
we're go - ing through chan - ges.
F
Am
D/A
Am7
E7/A
Am
C
Csus4
C
3fr
Csus4
C
(Female) It took so

C
Dm7/C
C
Csus4
C
Dm11
long to re - a - lise and I can still hear
C
Csus4
C
C
Dm/C
C
his last good - bye. (Male) Now all my days are filled with
C
Csus4
C
Dm
C
Csus4
fears, wish I could go back and change the years.
C
F
C/E
Dm
(Both) We're go - ing through chan - ges,

F
C/E
Dm
Fadd9
we're go - ing through chan - ges.
We're
Cadd9/E
Dm
G
F
go - ing through chan - ges.
Am
G
Am
G
Chan - ges, chan -
Am
G
C
- ges, chan - ges.

The Closer I Get To You

Words & Music by Reggie Lucas & James Mtume

E♭maj9
5fr
N.C.
Gm7
3fr
Cm7
3fr
3
(Male) Ooh, yeah, your love has cap - tured me.
let's give love a try.
A♭maj7
4fr
Gm7
3fr
B♭m7
1, 2. (Female) Ov - er and ov - er a - gain I try to tell my self that we
3. (Female) Sweet - er and sweet - er love grows, and Hea - ven's there, for those
A♭maj9
3fr
A♭maj7
4fr
B♭m7/E♭
6fr
E♭9
5fr
can nev - er be more than friends. And all the while in - side I
who fool the tricks of time with hearts in love will
A♭maj7
4fr
Gm7/C
3fr
N.C.
knew it was real: the way you
find true love in a

1.
Fm7
B♭11
4fr
E♭maj7
6fr
E♭maj9
5fr
N.C.
A♭maj7
4fr
Gm7
3fr
Cm7
3fr
make me feel.
E♭maj9
5fr
N.C.
Gm7
3fr
Cm7
3fr
2.
Fm7
A♭m6/C♭
A♭m6/B♭
spe - cial way.
3.
Fm7
D♭9
3fr
make me feel,
A♭add9/B♭
A♭m6/B♭
A♭maj7
4fr
Gm7/C
4fr
(Male)
(Female)
my ba - by, my ba - by, my ba - by,
(Female) my love,
ooh.

Verse 5:
Come a little closer, let me whisper in your ear,
'Cos I wanna tell you something.

Verse 6:
Move on in real close, so we can celebrate the way
We feel about each other's loving.

Dead Ringer For Love

Words & Music by Jim Steinman

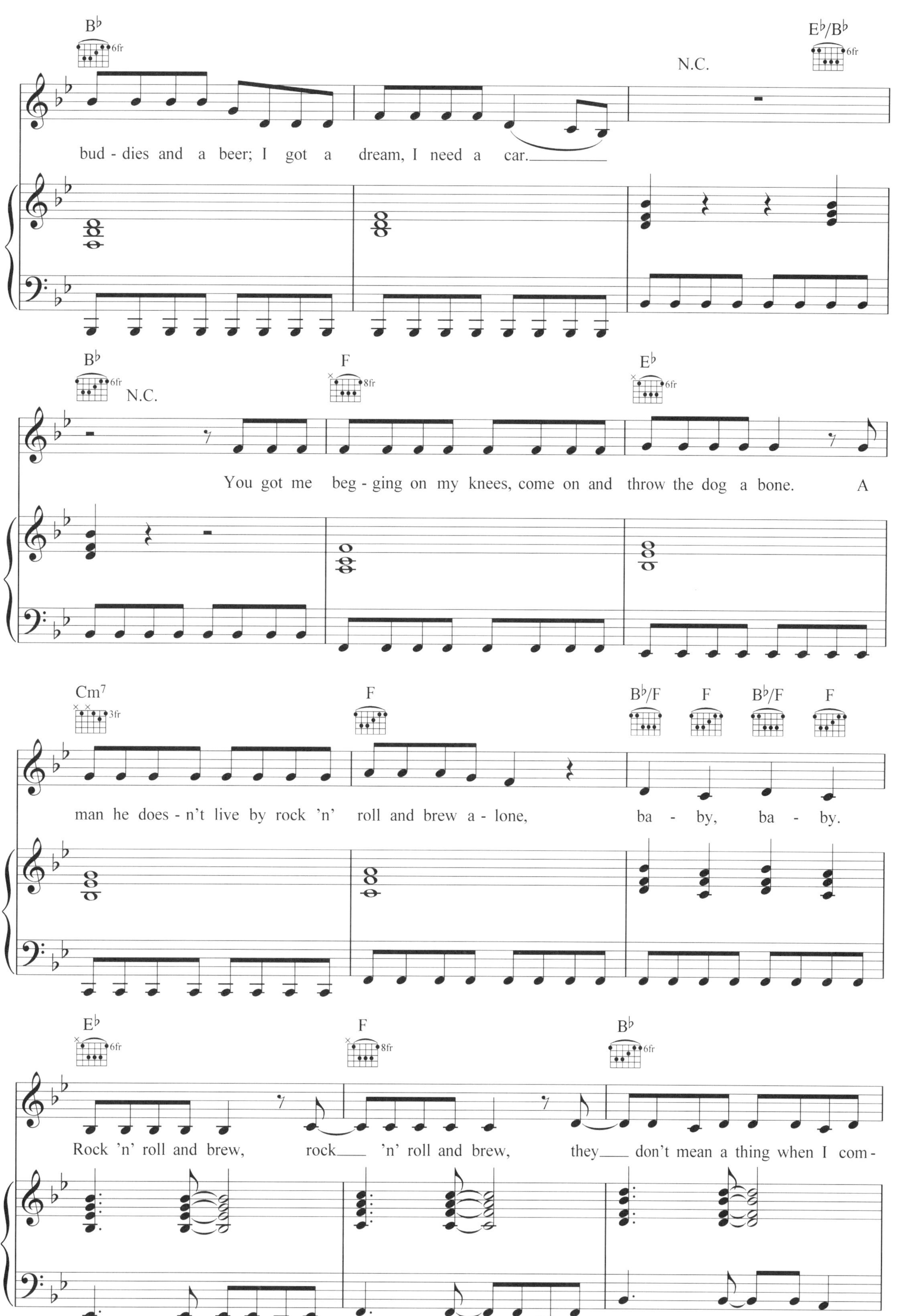
B♭
N.C.
E♭/B♭
6fr
bud - dies and a beer; I got a dream, I need a car.
B♭
N.C.
F
8fr
E♭
You got me beg - ging on my knees, come on and throw the dog a bone. A
Cm7
3fr
F
B♭/F
F
B♭/F
F
man he does - n't live by rock 'n' roll and brew a - lone, ba - by, ba - by.
E♭
F
B♭
Rock 'n' roll and brew, rock 'n' roll and brew, they don't mean a thing when I com -

Gm
3fr
E♭
6fr
F
8fr
-pare 'em next to you. Rock 'n' roll and brew, rock 'n' roll and brew; I
B♭
6fr
Gm
3fr
E♭
6fr
know that you and I we got bet - ter things to do. I don't know who you are, what you do or
F
8fr
Gm
3fr
where you go when you're not a - round.
I don't know
E♭
6fr
F
8fr
B♭
6fr
E♭
6fr
a - ny - thing a - bout you, ba - by, but you're ev - 'ry - thing I'm dream - ing of.

B♭
F
I don't know who you are, but you're a real dead ring - er for love,
E♭
F
B♭
E♭/B♭
B♭
E♭/B♭
a real dead ring - er for love.
B♭
E♭/B♭
B♭
E♭/B♭
B♭
2. (Female) Ev - er since I can re - mem - ber you been
(3.) since I can re - mem - ber I've been
hang - ing round this joint.
hang - ing round this joint.
N.C.
E♭/B♭
B♭
N.C.
You been
My
6fr
8fr

B♭
6fr
N.C.
E♭/B♭
6fr
try'n' to look a - way_ but now you fin - 'lly got the point.___
dad - dy nev - er not - iced, now he'll fin - 'lly get the point.___
B♭
6fr
N.C.
F
8fr
E♭
6fr
I don't have to know_ your name and I__ won't tell you what__ to do,___ but a
(Male) You've got me beg-ging on___ my knees, come on_ and throw the dog___ a bone,_ a
Cm7
3fr
F
B♭/F
F
B♭/F
F
girl she does - n't live by on - ly rock 'n' roll and brew, ba - by, ba - by,
man he does - n't live by rock 'n' roll and brew a - lone, (Both) ba - by, ba - by,
B♭/F
F
B♭/F
F
E♭
6fr
F
8fr
ba - by, ba - by. (Both) Rock 'n' roll and brew, rock___ 'n' roll and brew, (Male) they___
ba - by, ba - by. Rock 'n' roll and brew, rock___ 'n' roll and brew, I

B♭
6fr
Gm
3fr
E♭
6fr
__ don't mean a thing when I com - pare 'em next to you. (Both) Rock__ 'n' roll and brew, rock_
know that you and I we got bet - ter things to do. Rock__ 'n' roll and brew, rock_
F
8fr
B♭
6fr
Gm
3fr
__ 'n' roll and brew, (Male) I know that you and I, we got bet - ter things to do. I don't know
__ 'n' roll and brew, they don't mean a thing when I com - pare 'em next to you. (M) I don't know
E♭
6fr
F
8fr
Gm
3fr
who you are, what you do or where you go when you're not a - round.__
who you are, (F) what you do (M) or where you go (Both) when you're not a - round.__
E♭
6fr
F
8fr
(Female) I don't know an - y - thing a - bout you, ba - by, (Male) but you're ev -
I don't know an - y - thing a - bout you, ba - by, but you're ev -

B♭
6fr
E♭
6fr
B♭
6fr
To Coda
- 'ry - thing I'm dream - ing of.
(Female) I don't know who you are (B) but you're a
- ry - thing I'm dream - ing of.
I don't know who you are but you're a
F
8fr
E♭
6fr
F
8fr
B♭
6fr
real dead ring - er for love,
a real dead ring - er for love.
F
8fr
(Male) Ooh, you got the kind of legs that

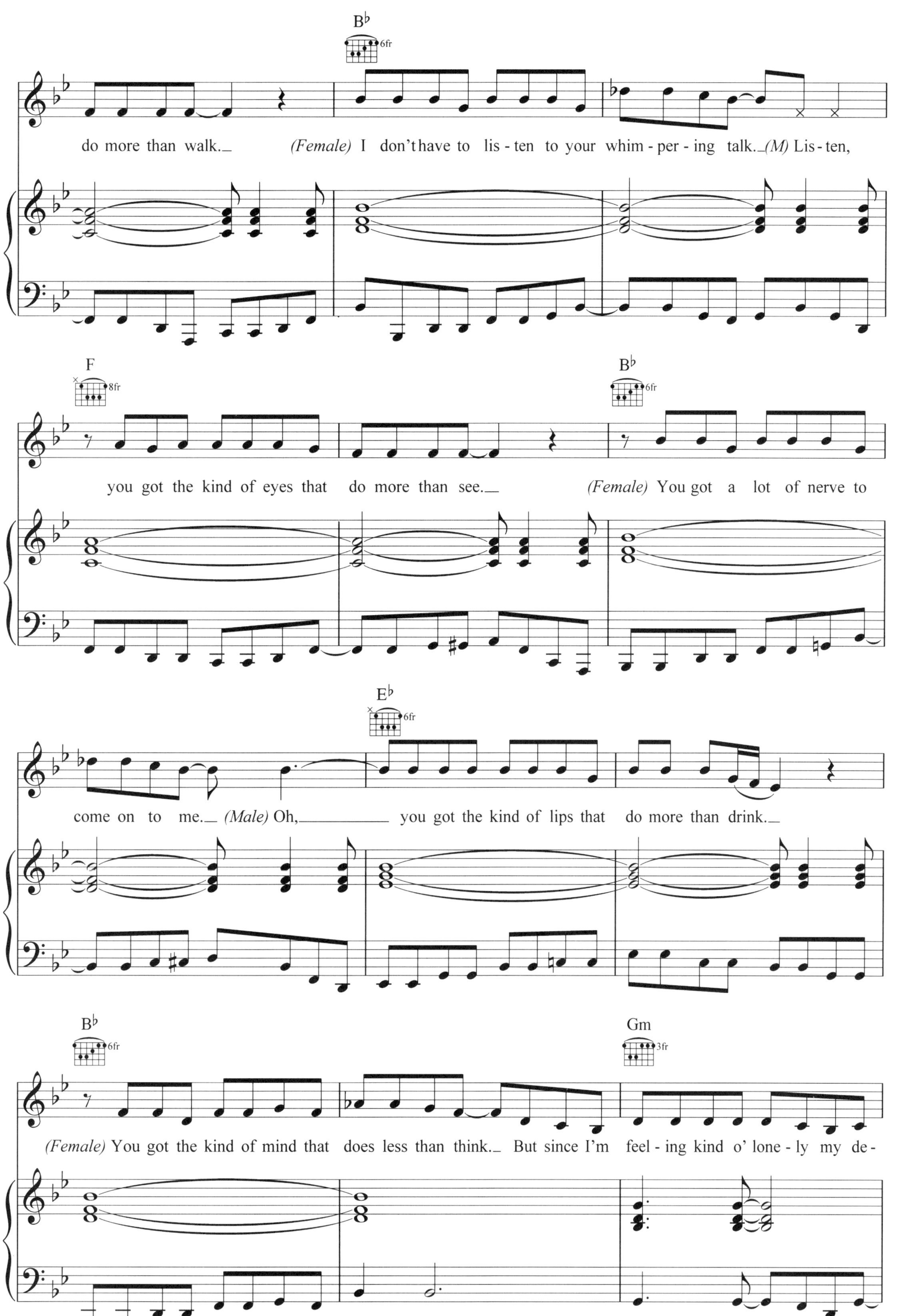
B♭
6fr
do more than walk. (Female) I don't have to lis-ten to your whim-per-ing talk. (M) Lis-ten,
F
8fr
B♭
6fr
you got the kind of eyes that do more than see. (Female) You got a lot of nerve to
E♭
6fr
come on to me. (Male) Oh, you got the kind of lips that do more than drink.
B♭
6fr
Gm
3fr
(Female) You got the kind of mind that does less than think. But since I'm feel-ing kind o' lone-ly my de-

Cm
3fr
-fen - ces are low. Why don't we give it a shot and get it rea - dy to go? I'm
E♭
6fr
F
8fr
look - ing for a - no - ny - mous and fleet - ing sa - tis - fac - tion. I wan - na tell my dad - dy I'll be
D.S. al Coda
miss - ing in ac - tion. 3. Ev - er
Coda
F
8fr
E♭
6fr
real dead ring - er for love, a
F
8fr
B♭
6fr
E♭/B♭
6fr
B♭
6fr
E♭/B♭
6fr
real dead ring - er for love.

B♭
E♭/B♭
6fr
Instrumental
Dead ring - er for love.
Dead ring - er for love.
1-11.
12.
Play 12 times
(Male) Dead ring - er
Dead ring - er.

Don't Know Much

Words by Cynthia Weil
Music by Barry Mann & Tom Snow

Original key: G♭ major

♩ = 65

F/A
G/B
C
F
G7
Csus4
C
and that may be all I need to know.
C
C/E
F/A
G/B
C
C/E
(Female) Look at these eyes, they nev - er see what mat - ters.
Look at these dreams,
F
G/B
Am7
Fmaj7
G
Em7
F
(Male) I don't know much,
but I know I love you;
(Female) so beat - en and so bat - tered.
Ooh.
But I know I love you;

F/A G/B C F G7 C Em7/B
and that may be all I need to know.
and that may be all I need to know.
Am7 D7 G Csus2 C
So ma - ny ques - tions still left un - an - swered,
F G7sus4 C Csus2 C
so much I've nev - er brok - en through.

Cm7
C7
B♭
E♭
E♭maj9
A♭
E♭/G
The on-ly truth I'll ev-er know
And when I feel you near me, some-times I see so clear-ly the on-ly truth I'll ev-er know
Cm
E♭/G
B♭
is me and you.
is me and you.
E♭
E♭/G
A♭/C
B♭/D
Look at this man, so blessed with in-spi-ra-tion.
2° Instrumental till *
2° Instrumental till *

E♭
E♭/G
E♭add9
A♭/C
B♭/D
Look at this soul, still search-ing for sal - va - tion.
*
Look at this soul.
*
Cm7
A♭maj7
B♭
Gm7
A♭
(1, 2.) I don't know much, but I know I love you;
(1, 2.) I don't know much, but I know I love you;
A♭/C
B♭/D
E♭
A♭
B♭7
1.
E♭
and that may be all I need to know.
and that may be all I need to know.
ad lib. instrumenal pick up

2.
E♭
B♭/D
Cm7
A♭maj7
B♭
know.
I don't know much,
know.
I don't know much,
Gm7
A♭
A♭/C
B♭/D
E♭
A♭
B♭
but I know I love you;
and that may be all there is to
but I know I love you;
and that may be all there is to
N.C.
rit.
E♭
know.
know.

Fairytale Of New York

Words & Music by Shane MacGowan & Jem Finer

1.
2.
Gsus4 C Gsus4
Gsus4 C F/C C F Gsus4
-bout you. 2. Got on a dreams come true.
♩ = ♩.
C G C F G C
3. (Female) They got
G Am F C
cars big as bars, they got riv - ers of gold; but the wind goes right through you, it's no
G C Am C F
place for the old. When you first took my hand on a cold Christ - mas Eve, you

C G C
pro - mised me Broad - way was wait - ing for me._ 4. You were hand - some. (Male) You were pret - ty, Queen
(5.) bum,___ you're a punk! (M) You're an
G C F G C
of New York Ci - ty. (Both) When the band fin - ished play - ing, they howled out for more. Sin -
old slut on junk,_ ly - ing there al - most dead on a drip on that bed!_ (F) You
G C F
- at - ra was swing - ing; all the drunks, they were sing - ing. We kissed on the cor - ner, then
scum - bag, you mag - got! you cheap, lous - y fag - got! Hap - py Christ - mas your arse! I pray

G C F C/E

danced through the night.
God it's our last. } *(Both)* The boys of the N. Y. P. D. choir were sing - ing, "Gal - way

Am C F G 1. C G

Bay". And the bells were ring - ing out for Christ - mas Day.

C
F
C
G
C
2. C
5. (Female) You're a
F
C
F
G
C
G
6. (Male) I could have
C
F
been some - one.
(F) Well, so could an - y - one.
You took my dreams
C
G
from me
when I first found you.
(M) I kept them

F
with me, babe; I put them with my own. Can't make it
C
F
G
C
all a - lone; I've built my dreams a - round you.
(Both) The
F
C/E
boys of the N. Y. P. D. choir still sing - ing "Gal - way
Am
C
F
G
rit.
C
Bay". And the bells are ring-ing out for Christ-mas Day.

Come What May

Words & Music by David Baerwald

C
Em/B
Am
Dsus4
D
F/G
G
more and more.
Lis- ten to my heart, can you hear it sing?
Tel- ling me to give you
mf
Csus4
C
G/B
Am
C/G
D/F♯
ev - 'ry - thing, sea - sons may change.
win- ter to spring.
But I
mp
C/G
G
C
G/B
Am
love you un - til the end of time
Come what may
D
C
come what may
I will love you un - til my

C/G
G
C
C
dy - - - - - ing day.
(Female) Su-dden-ly the world seems such
mp
Dsus4
D
F
C
G/B
Am
a per - fect place.
Su-dden-ly it moves with such a per - fect grace,
(Both) su-dden-ly my life does - n't seem
mf
Dsus 4
D
F maj7
C
G/B
Am
(Male)
such a waste.
(Female) It all re - volves a-round you
(Female) and there's no moun - tain too high, no
mp
mf
Dsus4
D
F/G
G
Csus4
C
G/B
Am
Am/G
ri - ver too wide,
sing out this song and I'll be there by your side,
storm clouds may ga - ther and

D/F♯
C/G
Fmaj7/G
G
stars may col - lide,
(Female) I love you
un - til the end of
(Male) but I love you
un - til the end of
C
G/B
Am
Dsus4
(Male)
(Female)
time come what may,
come what may
mp
f
D
C
C/G
G7
C
G/B
I will love you un - til my dy - ing day. Oh come what
Am
Dsus4
D
may, come what may
I will

C
G/B
C/E
F
Dm
F
love you will love you
su - dden-ly the world
seems such a per - fect place
p
A♭
4fr.
B♭
C
F/C
C
Come what may,
come what
ff
F/C
Am
F
may
I will love you
un - til my
C/G
G
C
dy - - ing
day.

I Knew You Were Waiting (For Me)

Words & Music by Simon Climie & Dennis Morgan

A
A/E
E
con - sumed by the sha - dows. I was crip - pled e - mo - tion - 'lly,
the hurt is ov - er; one touch and you set me free.
F♯m7
C♯m7
mmm.
(Male) Some - how I made it through the
(Male) I don't re - gret a sin - gle
F♯m7
C♯m7
heart - aches, yes I did; I es - caped.
mo - ment, no I don't. Look - ing back,
F♯m7
C♯m7
I found my way out of the dark - ness. I kept my faith,
when I think of all these dis - ap - point - ments, I just laugh,
4fr

A
N.C.
E
kept my faith. (Male)
I just laugh. (Female)
When the riv - er was deep, (M) I did - n't fal -
A
E
- ter; (Both) when the moun - tain was high, (M) I still be - lieved.
A
E
A
(Both) When the val - ley was low, (M) it did - n't stop me, oh no. (Both) I
F♯m
C♯m
4fr
N.C.
F♯m
A
N.C.
1.
E
A
knew you were wait - ing, I knew you were wait - ing for me. Uh, huh.

A/E
E
2. (Female) With an end - less des - ire,
2.
A/C♯
Am/C
E/B
C♯m7
4fr
So we were drawn to - geth - er through des - ti - ny.
A/C♯
Am/C
E/B
I know this love we share
N.C.
F♯m
C♯m
4fr
N.C.
was meant to be.
I knew you were wait - ing,

F♯m
C♯m
4fr
N.C.
F♯m
A
N.C.
knew you were wait - ing,
I knew you were wait - ing for me.
E
A
E
(M) I did - n't fal - ter,
I still be - lieved.
A
E
A
When the val - ley was low,
it did - n't stop me.
(Both) I
F♯m
C♯m
4fr
N.C.
F♯m
A
N.C.
Repeat ad lib. to fade
knew you were wait - ing,
I knew you were wait - ing for me.

Islands In The Stream

Words & Music by Barry Gibb, Maurice Gibb & Robin Gibb

C
real thing.
(Both) You do some - thing to me that I
(Both) But that won't hap - pen to us and we
can't ex - plain;
got no doubt;
hold me clos - er and I feel no pain. Ev - 'ry
too deep in love, and we got no way out. And the
Fsus2
C
beat of my heart, we got some - thing go - ing on.
mes - sage is clear; this could be the year of the real thing.
Fsus2
(Male) Ten - der love is blind; it re - quires a ded - i - ca - tion. (B) All
(Female) No more will you cry; ba - by, I will hurt you nev - er. (B) We

Fm6/A♭
6fr
C
this love we feel needs no con-ver-sa-tion. We ride it to-geth-er, uh-
start and end as one, in love for-ev-er. We can ride it to-geth-er, uh-
huh, from one love to an-oth-er, uh-huh.
huh, from one love to an-oth-er, uh-huh.
Is-lands in
C
F
Dm7
the stream, that is what we are. No one in be-tween; how can we
C
F
be wrong? Sail a-way with me to an-oth-er world, and we re-

1
C
Dm7
Dm7/G
ly on each oth - er, uh - huh, from one lov - er to an - oth - er, uh -
C
Em
Fsus2
Gsus
3fr
D.S.
huh.
2
Dm7
Dm7/G
C
Em
- er to an - oth - er, uh - huh.
Fsus2
Gsus
3fr
C
Em
I'll be al -

Fsus2
Gsus
3fr
3
Dm7
Dm7/G
- right, oh. Is - lands in - er to an - oth - er, uh -
C
Em
Fsus2
huh. I'll be al - right. Good - bye, to - night.
Gsus
3fr
C
Em
Good - night for now. Good - bye, to - night.
Fsus2
C/G
Gsus
3fr
C
Al - right, for now good - bye.

It Takes Two

Words & Music by William Stevenson & Sylvia Moy

- ing in love,___ (M) two can say how it real - ly feels.___
___ the pain,___ like a per - fect re - me - dy.___
sin - gle mov - ie some-thing real - ly kind of sweet.___
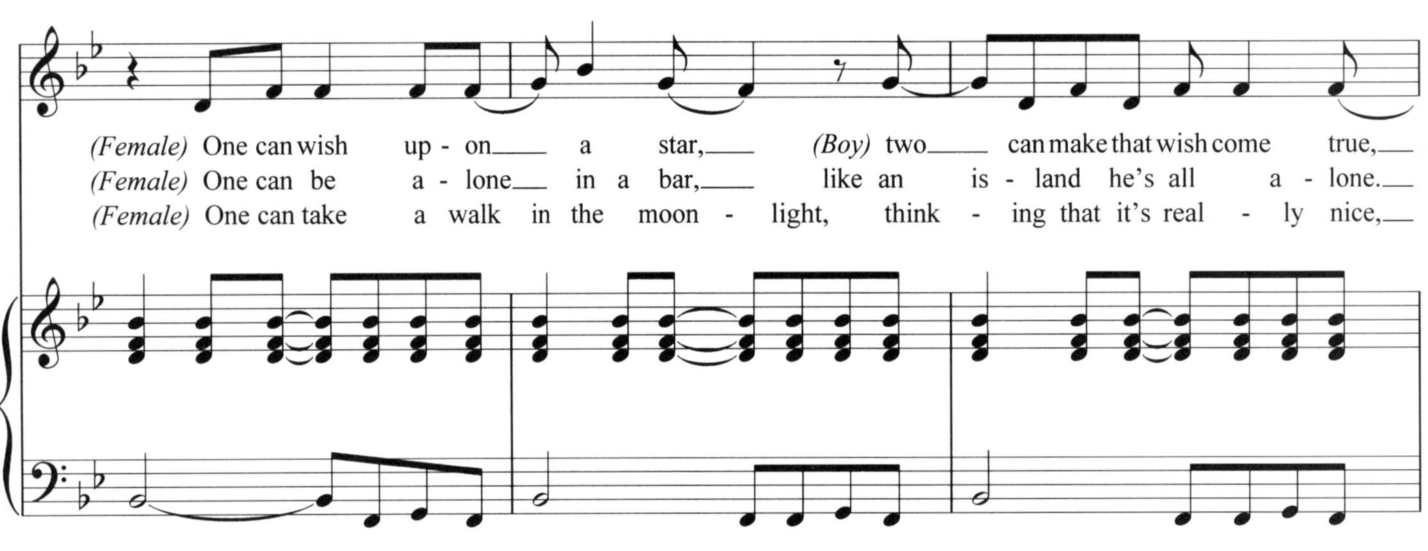
(Female) One can wish up - on___ a star,___ (Boy) two___ can make that wish come true,___
(Female) One can be a - lone___ in a bar,___ like an is - land he's all a - lone.___
(Female) One can take a walk in the moon - light, think - ing that it's real - ly nice,___
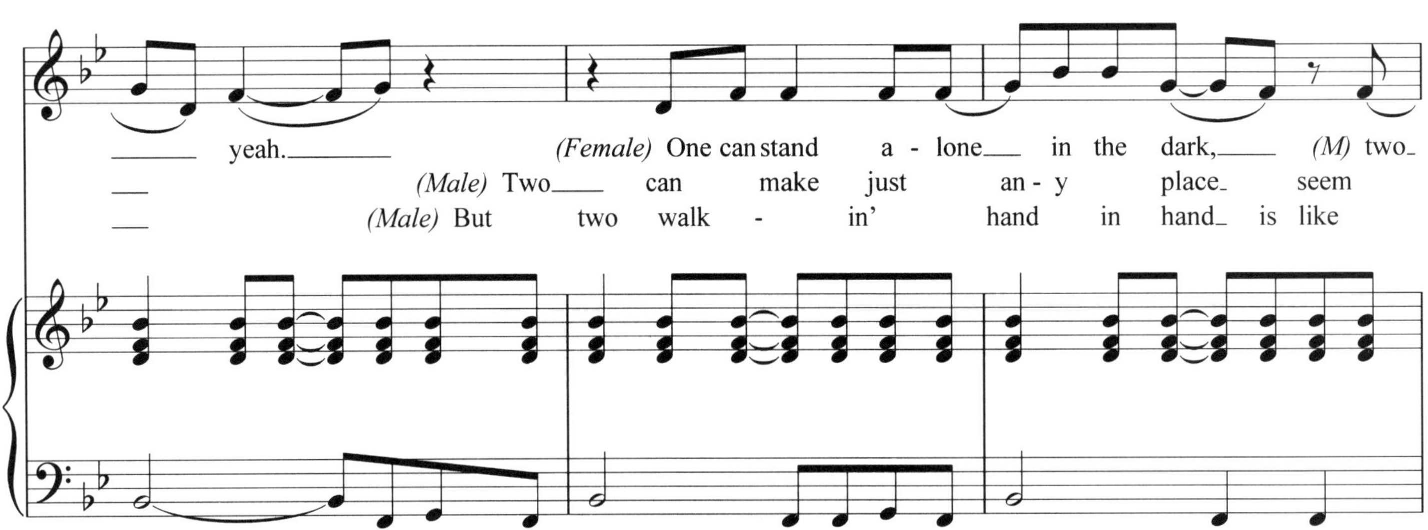
___ yeah.___ (Female) One can stand a - lone___ in the dark,___ (M) two_
___ (Male) Two___ can make just an - y place_ seem
___ (Male) But two walk - in' hand in hand_ is like

B♭7
___ can make the light shine through.___
just like be - ing home.___
add - ing just a pinch of spice.___
(Female)
(Male)
It takes two,___
E♭6
C7/E
F
Cm
3fr
___ ba - by;___
it takes two,___ ba - by:___
3
3
F
N.C.
B♭
___ me and you.___
It just takes___ two.___
B♭7
E♭6
___
It takes two___ ba - by;___

C7/E
F
Cm
it takes two, ba - by:
F
N.C.
to make a dream come true.
N.C.
B♭
Cm
B♭
Cm
B♭
Cm
B♭
Cm
B♭
Cm
It just takes two.
1.
B♭
Cm
B♭
2.
B♭
Cm
B♭

B♭
Wee, hoo ooh. woo-hoo hoo.
B♭7
E♭6
Woo, hoo.
F
N.C.
B♭
Just take two.
D.S. to fade
Just take two.
(F) Ooh.

Je T'aime... Moi Non Plus

Words & Music by Serge Gainsbourg

G
F
Em
G7
irrésolue.
Je vais, je
C
Fmaj7
G7sus4
Am
vais et je viens,
en-tre tes riens.
F
G9sus4
G7
C
Am
Fmaj7
Dm
Je vais et je viens,
en-tre tes riens.
Em
F
G7
N.C.
Play 6 times (6° fade to end)
Et je me re - tiens.

Verse 2:

(Female) Je t'aime, je t'aime
Oh oui je t'aime!
(Male) Moi non plus.
(Female) Oh mon amour…
Tu es la vague, moi l'òle nue

Tu vas, tu vas et tu viens,
Entre mes reins.
Tu vas et tu viens,
Entre mes reins,
Et je te rejoins.

Verse 3:

(Female) Je t'aime, je t'aime,
Oh, oui, je t'aime!
(Male) Moi non plus.
(Female) Oh mon amour…
(Male) Comme le vague irrésolue.

Je vais, je vais et je viens
Entre tes riens,
Je vais et je viens
Entre tes riens,
Et je me retiens.

Verse 4:

Istrumental
(Female) Tu vas, tu vas et tu viens entre mes riens,
Tu vas et tu viens
Entre mes riens
Et je te rejoins.

Verse 5:

(Female) Je t'aime, je t'aime,
Oh, oui, je t'aime!
(Male) Moi non plus.
(Female) Oh mon amour…
(Male) L'amour physique est sans issue.

Je vais, je vais et je viens
Entre tes riens,
Je vais et je viens,
Je me reteins...
(Female) Non! Maintenant viens!

Verse 6:

Instrumental to fade

Kids

Words & Music by Robbie Williams & Guy Chambers

E5
A
1.(F) Me no bub - bl - e - tious, (M) me smoke hea - vy tar.
2.(F) You've got a re - pu - ta - tion. (M) Well, I guess that can be ex - plored. (F) You're
E5
A
(F) Me be groov - in' slow - ly where you are.
danc - ing with the chair - man of the board. (M) Take ride on my
E5
A
(M) No - ti - fy your next of kin 'cos you're nev - er com - ing back.
twelve cy - lin - der sym - pho - ny, but if you got o - ther plans... (F) The
E5
A
(F) I've been drop - ping beats since Back in Black.
pur - pose of a wo - man is to love her man.
(M)
(F) } And we'll

E5
A
paint by num - bers till some - thing sticks. I
E5
A
don't mind do - in' it for the kids.
(Male) So come on:
E5
G6
Dsus2
(Both) jump on board, take a ride, yeah.
A5
B5
G
F♯7
(You'll be do - ing it al - right.) Jump on board, feel the high,

C
D
B5
yeah.
'Cos the kids are al - right.
E
G
D
A
E
(Male)
(Female) 2º only
I'm gon - na give it all of my lov - in',
it's gon - na take up all of my love.
G
D
A
E
I'm gon - na give it all of my lov - in',
it's gon - na take up all of my love.
E
A7
(F) Come down from the ceil - ing.
(M) I did - n't mean to get so high.
(F) I could - n't

E
D
A
do what I want-ed to do when my lips were dry.
(M) You
E
D
A7
can't just up and leave me. I'm a sing-er in a band.
(F) Well
E
A
I like drum-mers ba-by, you're not my bag.
E5
G6
Dsus2
(Both) Jump on board, take a ride, yeah.

A5
B5
G
(You'll be do - ing it al - right.) Jump on
F#7
C
board feel the high, yeah.
1.
2.
D
B
'Cos the kids are al - right.
E5
G5
3fr
3
(M) I'm an ho - na - ry Sean Con - ne - ry, born se - ven - ty four. There's on - ly one of me
(M)Press be ask - in' do I care for so - do - my? I don't know, yeah, pro - ba - bly.

A5
B5/F♯
sin - gle hand - ed - ly rais - ing the e - co - no - my. Ain't no chance of the re - cord comp - 'ny drop - pin' me.
I've been look - in' for se - ri - al mo - no - ga - my, not some bird that looks like Bil - ly Con - nel - ly.
E5
A
But for now I'm down with or - ni - tho - lo - gy, grab your bi - no - cu - lars, come fol - low me.
E5
A
I like to drink it up but nev - er like to sink it, uh, uh. I like to drink it up but nev - er like to sink it, uh, uh.
E5
A
Repeat ad lib. to fade
I like to drink it up but nev - er like to sink it, uh, uh. Uh uh uh uh uh uh uh uh uh uh uh uh.

Kinky Boots

Words & Music by Herbert Kretzmer & David Lee

F
C
F
C
N.C.
G
C
N.C.
bor - rowed from the brutes,(F) bor-rowed from the brutes: kin - ky boots.
gath - er - ing the fruits,(F) gath - er - ing the fruits: kin - ky boots.
G
C/G
G
G/F
G
Fash - ion ma - ga - zines say, "Wear 'em",(M) and you rush to o - bey, like the
Ad - ver - tis - ing men say, "Try 'em",(M) and you all run a - mok like a
G/B
C
G
D7
G
G/B
wo - men in the ha - rem! (F) Full length, half length, (M) ful - ly fash - ioned calf - length,
flock of sheep to buy 'em! (F) Sweet girls, street girls, (M) frum - py lit - tle beat girls,
C
G
D7
G
G/B
C
G
(F) brown boots, black boots, (M) pat - ent - leath - er jack - boots, (F) low boots, high boots,
(F) square girls, cool girls, (M) se - xy lit - tle school girls, (F) maid - en aunt - ies,

D7
G
G/F
G
N.C.
(M) love - ly lank - y thigh - boots: (F) we all dig those boots!
(M) May - fair de - bu - tant - es: (F) they all dig those boots!
C
C/E
F
C
F
Ev - 'ry - bo - dy's cra - zy 'bout those kin - ky boots, kin -
Ev - 'ry - bo - dy's rush - ing for those Rus - sian boots, (M) Rus -
C
N.C.
D9
2fr
G
1.
C
C/E
- ky boots, kin - ky boots. (M) And, wheth - er you're in eve - ning dress or
- sian boots, (F) kin - ky boots.
F
F♯dim
G7
C
N.C.
bath - ing suits,(F) you wear boots, boots, kin - ky boots.

2.
C
F
F♯dim
(Both) cov - er up those ten - der lit - tle ten - der foots
G7
with kin - ky, kin - ky,
Dm7
(M) Leath - er is so kin - ky!
(F) Come and get those
G7
C
kin - ky boots, boots, kin - ky boots.

A Little Time

Words & Music by Paul Heaton & David Rotheray

own, I need a lit - tle time to find my
free - dom, I need a lit - tle. (F) Fun - ny how quick the milk turns sour,
B♭ C F
is - n't it, is - n't it? Your face has been look - ing like that for hours,
B♭ C B♭ C C7
has - n't it, has - n't it? Pro - mis - es, pro - mis - es turn to dust,

F
Gm
fr3
B♭
To Coda
wed - ding bells just turn to rust.
Trust in - to mis -
8vb
C
1.
2.
B♭
- trust.
(M) 2. I need a lit - tle
(8vb)
Fmaj7

D.%. al Coda
(M) 3. I've had a lit - tle
Coda
C
Fmaj7
I had a lit - tle time to think it
ov - er. Had a lit - tle room to work it out.
I found a lit - tle
cour - age to call it off.
(M)
(F)
I've had a lit - tle time.

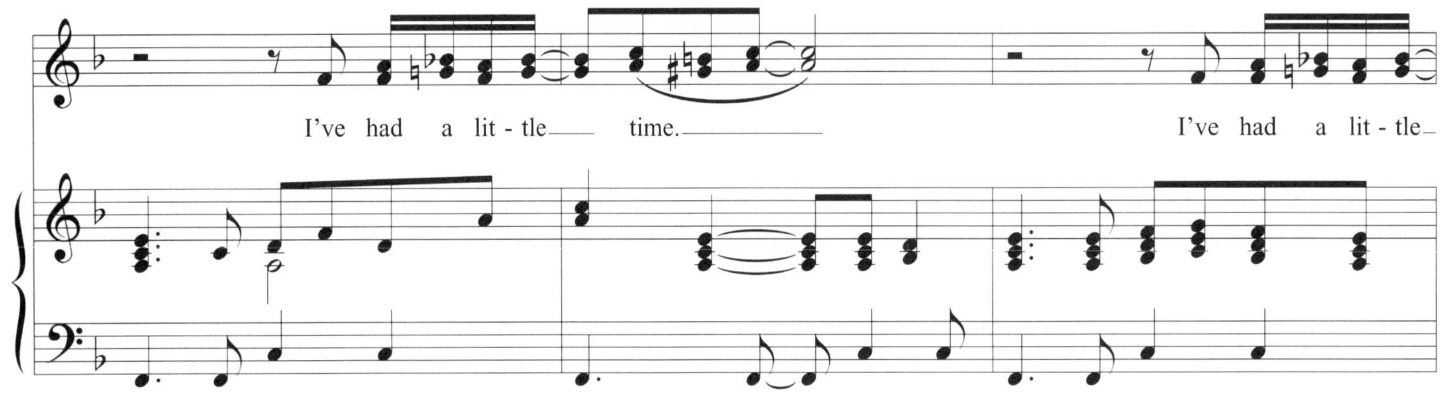

Verse 2:

(M) I need a little room to find myself,
I need a little space to work it out,
I need a little room all alone,
I need a little...

(F) You need a little room for your big head,
Don't you, don't you?
You need a little space for a thousand beds,
Won't you, won't you?
Lips that promise, fear the worst,
Tongue so sharp the bubble burst...
Just into unjust.

Verse 3:

(M) I've had a little time to find the truth,
I've had a little room to check what's wrong,
I've had a little time and I still love you,
I've had a little...

(F) You had a little time and you had a little fun,
Didn't you, didn't you?
When you had yours do you think I had none,
Do you, do you?
The freedom that you wanted back
Is yours for good, I hope you're glad,
Sad into un-sad.

I had a little time to think it over *etc.*

No More Tears (Enough Is Enough)

Words & Music by Paul Jabara & Bruce Roberts

Bm7/E Em7 Am7 G/B Bm7/E Em Em/D
per - fect lov - er, but he turned out to be like ev - 'ry oth - er man I
rit. a tempo
F Fadd9 F E7 Cadd9 B7aug B♭13 A7♭5
(V2) (V1) loved, I loved.
(V1) Rain-ing, pour-ing.
(V2) Rain - ing, pour - ing,
(V2) there's no - thing left for us
Dm7 Em7 A♭/B♭ Dm7 G13♭9 N.C.
rit.
here;
(V1) Mmm.
(V1) (V2) and we won't waste a - no - ther (V1) tear.
♩ = 136
Am Dm 5fr
(etc.)
(V2) Ah, ha, ha, ha, yeah.

Am
Aaug
2fr
A
A7
(V2) If
Dm
5fr
Gm
3fr
you've had e - nough, don't put up with his stuff, don't you do it.
Dm
5fr
(V1) Now if you've had your fill, get the cheque, pay the bill, you can
Gm
3fr
C
3fr
do it.
(V2) Tell him to just

C♯dim
4fr
Dm
5fr
get out, (V1) no - thing left to talk a - bout.
C
3fr
C♯dim
4fr
Dm
5fr
D7
5fr
(V2) Pack his rain - coat, show him out, (Both) just look him in the eye and (V1) (V2) sim-
Gm
3fr
- ply shout: E - nough is e - nough, is e - nough,
Cm
3fr
D7
5fr
I can't go on, I can't go on no long - er. E -

Gm
3fr
Cm
3fr
-nough is e - nough, is e - nough, I want him out, I want him out
D7
5fr
E♭maj7
6fr
that door now. (V1) I al - ways dreamed I'd find the
Dm7
5fr
E♭maj7
6fr
3
per - - fect lov - er, but he turned
Dm7
5fr
E♭maj7
6fr
3
3
out to be like ev - 'ry oth - er man I loved,
(V2) I had no

Dm7
5fr
E♭maj7
6fr
I loved,
I loved,
choice from the start.
I've got-ta
Dm7
5fr
I loved,
I
lis-ten to my heart.
tear-ing us a-
D
loved.
-part.
(Both) E-
Gm
3fr
Cm
3fr
-nough is e-nough is e-nough, I can't go on, I can't go on

D7
5fr
Gm
3fr
no longer. Enough is enough, is enough, I want him out,
Cm
D7
I want him out that door now.
(V2) Good-bye, mister,
good-bye, good-bye
mister.
Good-bye sugar.

Gm
3fr
Cm/G
3fr
(Both) No more tears.
Gm
3fr
Cm/G
3fr
(V1) No more tears,
Gm
3fr
Cm/G
3fr
(V2) no more tears.
Gm
3fr
Gm9
3fr
Cm7
3fr
(E - nough is e - nough is e - nough is e - nough is e - nough is e - nough is e - nough
Lead vocals ad lib.

Cm
3fr
Gm
3fr
Gm7
3fr
is e-nough is e-nough is e-nough is e-nough is e-nough is e-nough
Cm
3fr
Gm
3fr
is e-nough is e-nough is e-nough is e-nough is e-nough is e-nough is e-nough is e-nough
Cm
3fr
Gm
3fr
is e-nough is e-nough is e-nough is e-nough is e-nough is e-nough
Cm
3fr
Gm
3fr
is e-nough is e-nough is e-nough is e-nough is e-nough is e-nough!)

On My Own

Words & Music by Carole Bayer Sager & Burt Bacharach

B♭6(no 5th)
B♭maj7
B♭6(no 5th)
B♭
Some - thing in my heart al - ways knew I'd be
Now we're up to talk - in' di - vorce and we
You walked out and there went my life; I don't
F(addG)/C
To Coda
ly - ing here be - side you.
were - n't e - ven mar ried.
want to live with - out you.
On my
(Female) On my
On my
Gm7/C
F(addG)/C
own, on my own,
own, once a - gain,
own, on my own,
1.
Gm7/C
on my own.
one more
on my

2. Gm7/C
F
time.
By my-self;
F(no 3rd)
B♭maj7
C/B♭
C
no one said it was eas-y,
F
F(no 3rd)
B♭maj7
(Male) but it once was so eas-y.
Gm7
3fr.
(Female) Well, I be-lieved in love, now here
Am7
Dm7
I stand;
(Both) I won-der why

Gm7/C
Vocal ad lib
(Female) I'm on my own.
(On my
F(addG)/C
Gm7/C
D.S. al Coda
own, on my own.)
Repeat and fade (vocal ad lib on repeats)
Coda
Gm7/C
F(addG)/C
own, on my own, on my
Gm7/C
F(addG)/C
F6(no 5th)/C
Vocal ad lib
own, by my - self.
(On my

Reunited

Words & Music by Dino Fekaris & Freddie Perren

1.
2.
Fm7
G♭m7
C♭11
D♭maj9
D♭
B♭11
B♭m
E♭m9
G♭m9
Dmaj9
3fr
4fr
6fr
lone - some and sad. I re - al - ise I love you 'cos I want you back, hey, hey.
learn - ing so much; I know now that I love you 'cos I
need your touch, hey, hey. (Both) Re - un - it - ed, and it feels so good.
Re - un - it - ed, 'cos we un - der - stood (Female) (Male) there's one per - fect fit and, sug - ar,
this one is it. We both are so ex - ci - ted 'cos we're re - un - it - ed, hey, hey.

D♭maj9
B♭m
E♭m
Em7/A
A
Dmaj9
D6
3. (Female) I sat here star - ing at the same old wall, came back to life just when I got your call. I wished I could climb right through the te - le - phone line, and
4. (Male) I can't go cheat - ing, ho - ney, I can't play. I found it ve - ry hard to stay a - way. As we re - mi - nisce on pre - cious mo - ments like this, I'm
B11
Bm7
Em7
F♯m7
Gm7

1.
2.
C11
3fr
give you what you want so you will
glad we're back to-geth-er 'cos I
still be mine, hey, hey.
missed your kiss, hey, hey.
Dmaj9
4fr
D
5fr
B11
5fr
(Both) Re-un-it-ed, and it feels so good.
Re-un-it-ed, 'cos we
Bm
7fr
Em9
5fr
un-der stood
(Female)
(Male)
there's one per-fect fit and, sug-ar, this one is it. We
Gm9
3fr
C11
3fr
E♭maj9
5fr
Dmaj9
4fr
both are so ex-ci-ted 'cos we're re-un-it-ed, hey, hey.

Bm
7fr
Em
7fr
Fm7/B♭
B♭
(Female)
(Male)
Oh.
E♭maj9
5fr
E♭
6fr
(Male) Lov - ing lov - er, this is so - lid love.
C11
3fr
Cm
3fr
(Female) And you're ex - act - ly what I'm dream - ing of.
Fm9
(Male) All through the day (Female) and all through the night
(Female)
(Male)
I'll

A♭m9
D♭11
F♭maj9
give you all the love I have with all my might, hey, hey.
E♭maj9
E♭
C11
Re-un-it-ed... and it feels so good.
(Female) Re-un-it-ed, (F) 'cos we
(Male) Re-un-it-ed.
Cm
Fm9
fade out
un-der-stood. (Female) (Male) there's one per-fect fit and, sug-ar, this one is it. We
A♭m9
D♭11
F♭maj9
E♭maj9
both are so ex-ci-ted 'cos we're re-un-it-ed, hey, hey.

Senza Una Donna (Without A Woman)

Words & Music by Frank Musker & Adelmo Fornaciari

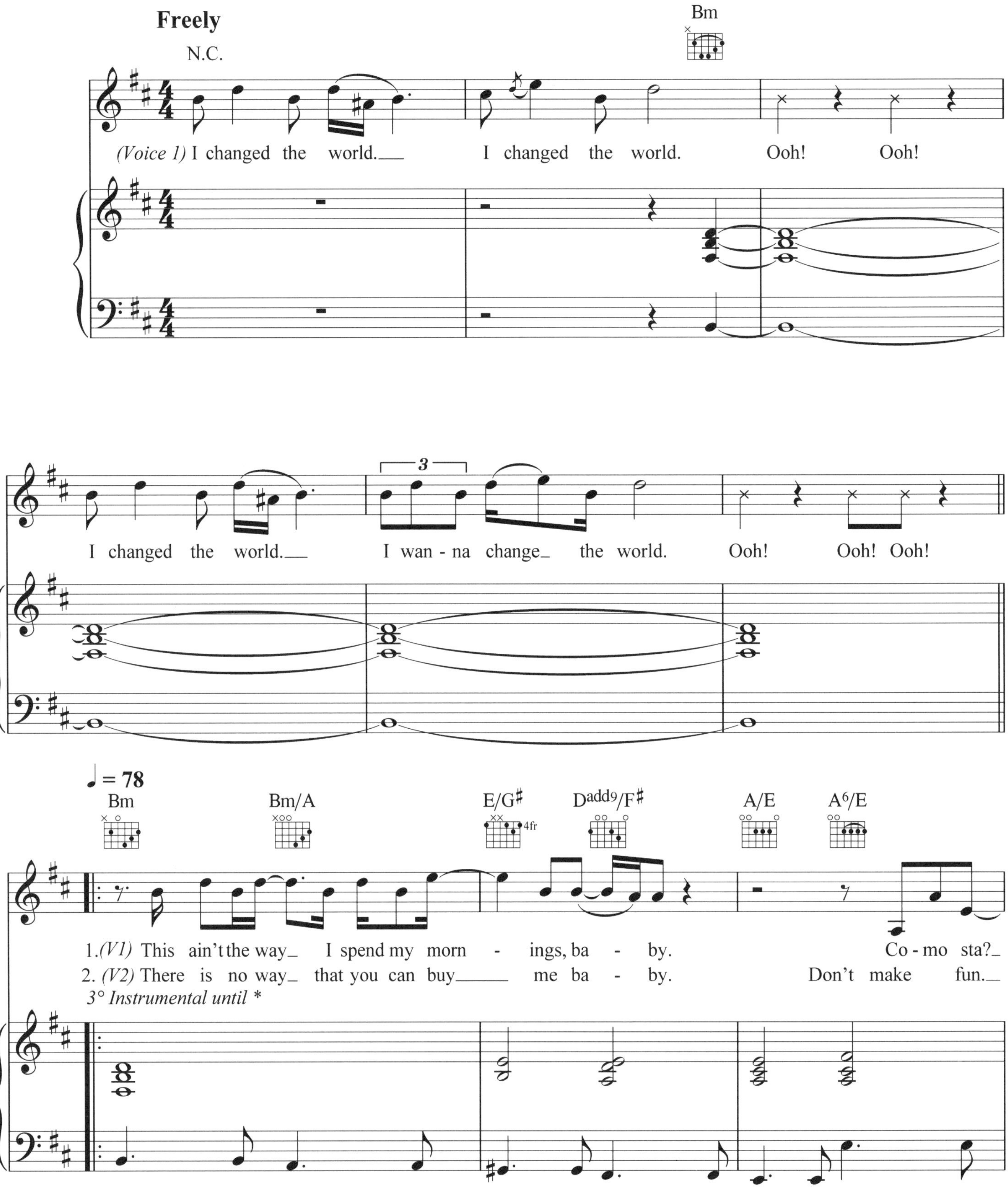

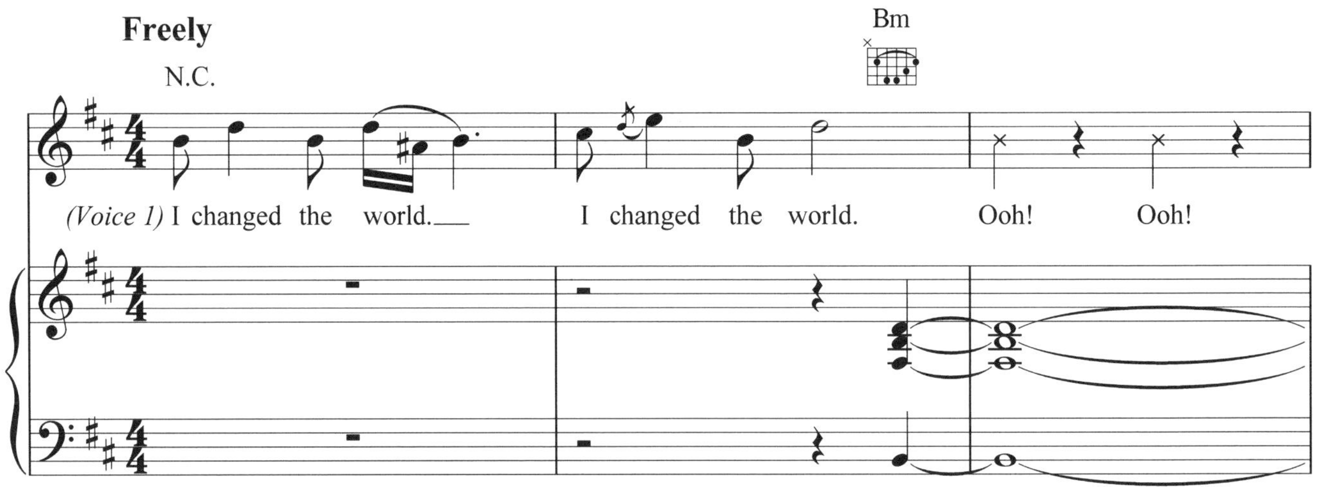

Freely
N.C.
Bm
(Voice 1) I changed the world. I changed the world. Ooh! Ooh!
I changed the world. I wan - na change the world. Ooh! Ooh! Ooh!
♩ = 78
Bm
Bm/A
E/G♯
Dadd9/F♯
A/E
A6/E
4fr
1.(V1) This ain't the way I spend my morn - ings, ba - by. Co - mo sta?
2. (V2) There is no way that you can buy me ba - by. Don't make fun.
3° Instrumental until *

A/E
A6/E
Bm
Bm/A
E/G♯
Dadd9/F♯
4fr
(V2) You been with him, now you come back, my la - dy.
(V1) You got to dig a lit - tle deep - er la - dy.
A/E
A6/E
A/E
A6/E
Bm
What's he like?
(Girl) In the heart? (V1) Yeah, if you have one
(V1) I just sit
(V2) Here's my heart,
* (V1) I stay here
A6
Gmaj7
A6
and watch the o - cean by my - self.
Even doing my own cooking.
feel the pow - er. (V1) Look at me: (V2) Look at me
(V1) I'm a flower.
and watch the o - cean. (V1) Don't know why (V2) Don't know why (V1) I keep on talk - ing. (V2) I keep on talk - ing
Bm
A6
Gmaj7
(V2) You can laugh, yeah, you're for - giv - en; but I'm no long - er fright - ened
(V2) You can laugh, yeah, you're for - giv - en; but (V1) I'm no long - er fright - ened
(V1) You may laugh you're for - giv - en; but (V2) I'm no long - er fright - ened

A6
D
Asus4/C♯
Bm
A
2fr
to be liv - ing
to be liv - ing
to be liv - ing
sen - za u - na don - na: (V1) no more pain and no sor - row. (V2) Sen - za u - na
D
A/C♯
G
A
don - na, I'll make it through to - mor - row (V1) Sen - za u - na
1.
D
Asus4/C♯
Bm
A
D
A/C♯
2° tacet
don - na, (V1) giv - ing me tor - ture and bliss. With - out a wo - man,
2.
Gmaj7
A
F♯7/A♯
G
D/F♯
A
F♯7/A♯
bet - ter like this. Ooh.

3.
G D/F♯ A
wo - man, vie - ni qui. (V2) Come on in… (Both) Sen - za u - na
D Asus4/C♯ Bm A D A/C♯
2fr
don - na, (V1) I don't know what might fol - low. (Sen - za u - na don na,) (V2) Oh, but may -
G A D Asus4/C♯
2fr
- be from to - mor - row. (Sen - za u - na don - na,) (V1) giv - ing me
Bm A G D/F♯ D
tor - ture and bliss. (B) Ooh.

Sisters Are Doin' It For Themselves

Words & Music by Annie Lennox & David A. Stewart

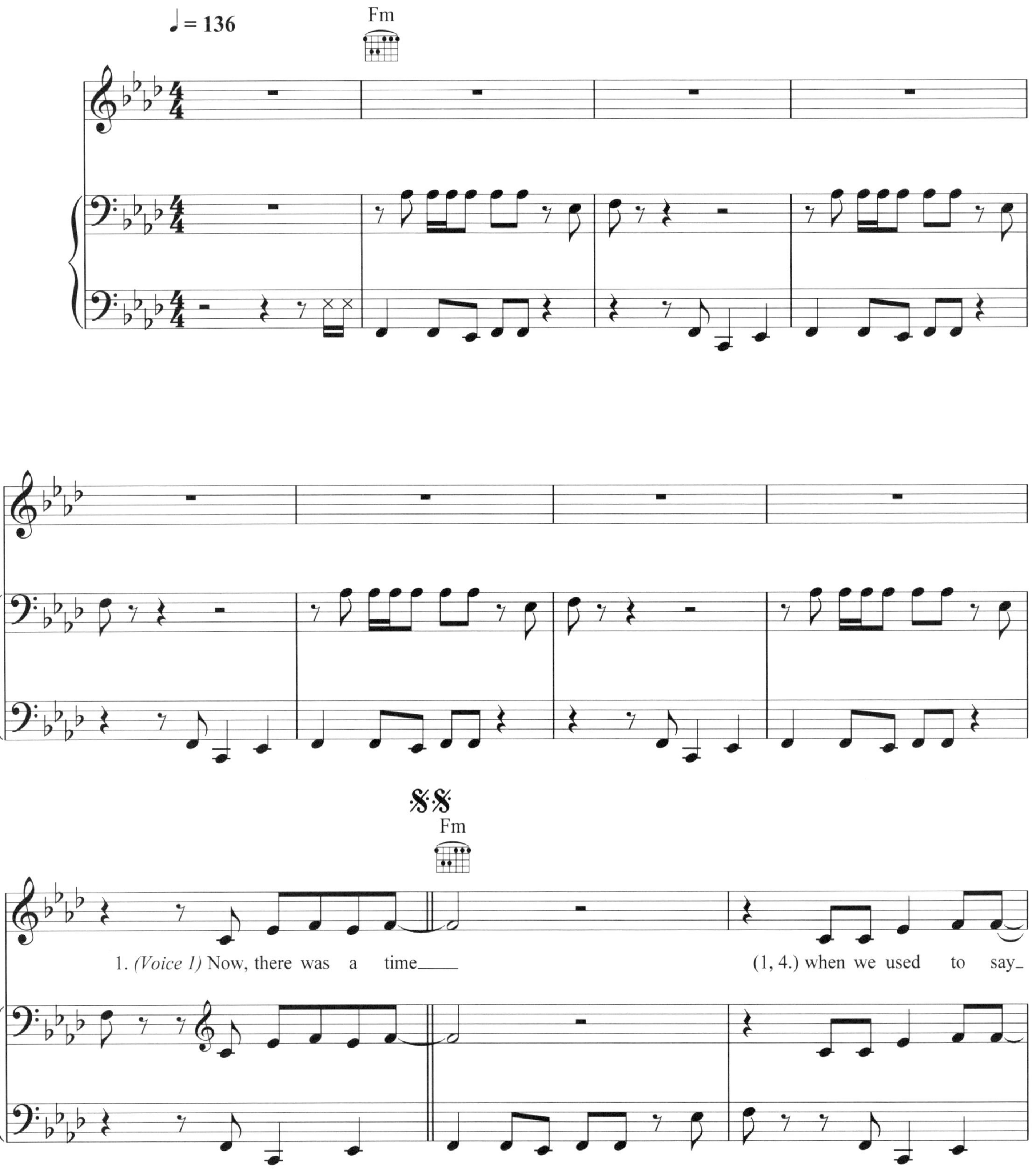

𝄋𝄋

Fm

1. *(Voice 1)* Now, there was a time (1, 4.) when we used to say

that be-hind ev-'ry great man there had to be a
great wo-man. (Voice 2) But oh, in these times of change
you know that it's no long-er true. (Both) So we're com-in' out of the kit-
-chen 'cos there's some-thing we for-got to say to you. We say:
C
3fr
E♭
6fr

A♭
4fr
B♭
6fr
A♭/C
8fr
Fm7
8fr
sis - ters are do - in' it for them - selves,
stand - in' on their
own two feet
and ring - in' on their own bells.
To Coda II
We say
sis - ters are do - in' it for them - selves.
To Coda I
C7sus4
2. (V1) Now, this is a song
Fm
(V2) to ce - le - brate,
(3.) - fe - ri - or sex has got a new ex - te - ri - or.
3

(Both) the cons - cious li - be - ra - tion of the fe -
(V1) We got doc - tors, law - yers, po - li - ti - cians too.
- male state.
(V2) Mo - thers, daugh - ters and their daugh - ters too,
(V2) Ev - 'ry - bo - dy take a
yeah.
look a - round.
(V1) Wo - man to wo -
(V1) Can you see, can you see, can you
- man we're sing - ing with you.
see, there's a wo - man right
1.
3. (V2) The in -

2.
C7
3fr
E♭
6fr
D.S. al Coda I
Coda I
C9sus4
next to you.
We say:
D♭
4fr
B♭7
(V2) We ain't mak - in' sto - ries, (V1) Ooh, we ain't lay - in' plans.
D♭
4fr
(V2) Don't you know that a man still loves a
B♭7
C7
3fr
wo - man? (V1) Ooh, and a wo - man still loves a man? (V2) Just the same, yeah.

Fm
1-3.
Play 4 times
Instrumental ad lib.
4.
E♭
B♭/D
D♭
Fm/C
A♭
(Both) Sis - ters are
B♭
A♭/C
Fm7
C7sus4
D.S.S. al Coda II
do - in' it for them - selves.
4. (V1) There was a time
Coda II
A♭
B♭
A♭/C
Fm
Repeat ad lib. to fade
Sis - ters are do - ing it for them - selves.

Some Velvet Morning

Words & Music by Lee Hazlewood

F♯m
F♯m6
F♯m
A
straight,
I'm gon-na
op - en up__ your_
F♯m
C♯m7
4fr
gate;
and may - be
tell
you 'bout
F♯m
A
F♯m
A
Phae - dre,
and how she gave_
me life,
and how she made_
it
F♯m
A
in.
Some
vel - vet
morn - ing
when I'm_

F♯m
F♯m6
F♯m
straight.
E
B
E
(1.) (Female) Flow - ers grow - ing on a hill, dra - gon -
(2.) (Female) Flow - ers are the things we know, sec - rets
B
A
- flies on daf - fo - dils:
are the things we grow;
learn from us
B
A
B
ve - ry much, look at us but do not

F♯
N.C.
touch. Phae - dre is my name.
F♯m
1.
2.
F♯m
3. (Male) Some vel - vet
A
F♯m
E
morn - ing when I'm straight… (Female) Flow - ers grow - ing
B
F♯m
A
F♯m
on a hill… (Male) I'm gon-na op - en up your gate…

E
B
(Female) Dra - gon - flies and daf - fo - dils…
C♯m7
4fr
F♯m
A
(Male) And may - be tell you'bout Phae - dre… (Female) Learn from
B
A
us ve - ry much… (Male) And how she gave me
F♯m
fade
A
B
life… (Female) Look at us but do not touch.

Somethin' Stupid

Words & Music by C. Carson Parks

F♯m7
B7
F♯m7
B7
F♯m7
B7
F♯m7
ev-'ning with me,
and if we go some place to dance I
B7
F♯m7
B7
E
E6
know that there's a chance you won't be leav-ing with me.
Emaj7
E6
E7
Bm7
E7
Bm7
Then af-ter-wards we drop in-to a qui-et lit-tle place and have a
A
C7
F♯m7
B7
drink or two,
and then I go and spoil it all by

F♯m7
9fr
B7
7fr
E
7fr
E6
6fr
Emaj7
7fr
E6
6fr
say - ing some - thin' stu - pid like, "I love you."
I can
E7
7fr
Bm7
7fr
E7
7fr
Bm7
7fr
see it in your eyes that you des - pise the same old lies you heard the
Amaj7
7fr
A6
7fr
Amaj7
7fr
A6
7fr
F♯7
9fr
C♯m7
9fr
night be - fore,
and though it's just a line to you, to
F♯7
9fr
B7
7fr
B7♯5
7fr
me it's true and nev - er seemed so right be - fore.
I

E
E6
Emaj7
E6
Emaj7
7fr
6fr
7fr
6fr
7fr
prac - tise ev - 'ry day to find some cle - ver lines to say to make the
(2° Instrumental until *)
F♯m7
B7
F♯m7
B7
F♯m7
9fr
7fr
9fr
7fr
9fr
mean - ing come true,
but
B7
F♯m7
B7
F♯m7
B7
7fr
9fr
7fr
9fr
7fr
then I think I'll wait un - til the ev - 'ning gets late and I'm
a -
E
E6
Emaj7
E6
E
E7
Bm7
7fr
6fr
7fr
6fr
7fr
7fr
7fr
-lone with you.
*
The time is right, your per - fume fills my

E7
7fr
Amaj7
7fr
A6
7fr
C
8fr
head, the stars get red and, oh, the night's so blue,
and
F♯m7
9fr
B7
7fr
F♯m7
9fr
B7
7fr
then I go and spoil it all by say - ing some - thin' stu - pid like, "I
1.
2.
E
7fr
E6
6fr
Emaj7
7fr
E6
6fr
E
7fr
love you."
love you."
C
8fr
E
7fr
C
8fr
Repeat to fade
I love you.
I

Something's Gotten Hold Of My Heart

Words & Music by Roger Cook & Roger Greenaway

D♭ C7 Fm E♭ D♭ C7
fr3
way through my dreams like a knife,— turn-ing me up,— and turn-ing me down,—
Fm E♭ D♭ C7 Fm
fr3
— mak - ing— me smile— and mak-ing me frown.
E♭
fr3
In a world that was small,— I once lived in a time—
A♭ D♭ C7 Fm
fr4
— that was peace with no trou-ble at all.— But then you came my

E♭
Fm
E♭
way,
and a feel - ing un - known
shook my heart, make me
B♭
E♭
B♭
E♭
B♭
want you to stay.
All of my nights
and all of my days,
D♭
C7
Fm
(Voice 2) I've got - ta tell you know. Some - thing's got - ten hold of my hand,
E♭
D♭
C7
Fm
drag - ging my soul
to a beau - ti - ful land,
yeah.

Fm
E♭
fr3
Some - thing has in - va - ded my night,
paint - ing my
D♭
C7
Fm
E♭
fr3
sleep with a col - our so bright.
Chang - ing the grey,
D♭
C7
Fm
E♭
fr3
D♭
C7
chang-ing the blue,
scar - let for me
and scar - let for
F
B♭
you.

F
Dm
G
G7
(Voice 1) I've got to know if this is the real
thing.
(Voice 2) I've got to know what's mak - ing my heart
sing, woah
yeah yeah yeah yeah yeah yeah.
C7
(Voice 1) You

smile and I am lost for a life - time, (Both) each min - ute spent with you is the right
time, ev - 'ry hour yeah, ev - 'ry day yeah, you
touch me and my mind goes a - stray yeah, and ba - - - -
by and ba - - - - by yeah.

Fm
E♭
D♭
C7
(Voice 1) Some-thing's got-ten hold of my hand, drag-ging my soul to a beau-ti-ful land,
fr3
Fm
E♭
yeah, some-thing has in-va-ded my night, paint-ing my
D♭
C7
Fm
E♭
D♭
C7
sleep with a col-our so bright. (Both) Chang-ing the grey, chang-ing the blue,
Fm
E♭
D♭
C7
F
rall.
scar-let for me and scar-let for you.

Time To Say Goodbye (Con Te Patiro)

Words & Music by Lucio Quarantotto & Francesco Sartori

Gadd9
D
Em
C
D
ten.
Su le fi-ne-stre mo-stra a tut-ti'il mio cu-ore che hai ac-ce-so.
mf
Chiu-di dentro me la lu-ce che hai in con-tra-to per stra-da.
a tempo
G
Time to say good-bye, pa-e-si che non ho
mai, ve-du-to e vis-su-to con me, a-des-so si, li vi-

G D Em C G D
vrò con te, par-ti-rò su na-vi per ma-ri che io lo
Em C G C D
so, no, no, non e-si-sto-no più, it's time to say good-bye.
poco rit.
G
(Male) Quan-do sei lon-ta-na sog-no al-l'o-riz-zon-te e man-can le pa-ro-le.
C D Am/C Bm/D C D Em
E io si, lo so che sei con me, con me, tu mia lu-na, tu sei qui con me
mf mf mf mp mp mp

C D Am/C Bm/D Em D G D
rall.
a tempo 1
mi-o so-le tu sei qui con me, con me, con me, con me. Time to say good-
mf mf mf
Em C G D Em C
-bye, pa-e-si che non ho mai, ve-du-to e vis-su-to con
G C D G D Em C
me a-des-so si, li vi-vrõ con te. Par-ti-rõ su
f
G D Em C G C D
na-vi per ma-ri che io lo so, no, no, non e-si-sto-no piu. (Both) Con te io li ri-vi-

A E F♯m D A E
vrò con te par - ti - rò su na - vi per ma - ri che io lo
ff
F♯m D A D E A E
so, no, no non e - si - sto - no più. Con - te io li ri - vi - vrò con te par - ti -
fff
F♯m D A E F♯m D
rò.
A D E Dm Em C D A
rall.
Io con te.
f

To All The Girls I've Loved Before

Words by Hal David
Music by Albert Hammond

Am7/D
D7
To Coda
G
C/G
1. G
song to all the girls I've loved be-fore.
know, to all the girls I've loved be-fore.
song to all the girls I've
2. (Voice 2) To all the girls I
2. G
C/G
G
(Both) The winds of change are al-ways blow - ing
and ev-'ry time I tried to
cresc.
f
Am7
Am7/D
D7
stay.
The winds of change con-tin-ued blow - ing,
Am7/D
D7
G
C/G
G
D.S. al Coda
and they just car-ried me a - way.
3. (Voice 1) To all the girls who
dim.

Coda
C/G
G
E♭7sus
A♭
loved be-fore.
4. (Voice 2) To all the girls who cared for me;
(5, 6.) loved be-fore;
cresc.
mf
B♭m7
who filled my nights with ec-sta-sy;
(V1) who trav-eled in and out our door;
they live with-in my
(V2) we're glad they came a-
B♭m7/E♭
E♭7
1. A♭
D♭/A♭
heart; I'll al-ways be a part of all the girls I've loved be-fore.
long; (V1) we ded-i-cate this song (B) to all the girls we've
To next strain
2. D♭/A♭
(Both) The winds of change are al-ways loved be-fore.
6. (Voice 1) To all the girls we've
cresc.

3.
F♭
G♭
A♭
Fine
loved
be - fore.
8va
dim. e molto rit.
pp
D♭/A♭
A♭
B♭m7
blow - ing
and ev - 'ry time I tried to stay.
3
f
B♭m7/E♭
E♭7
B♭m7/E♭
F♭7
The winds of change con-tin - ued blow-ing,
and they just car-ried me a -
F♭
A♭
D.S.S.
way.
5. (Voice 2) To all the girls we've
dim.

Under Pressure

Words & Music by David Bowie, Freddie Mercury, Roger Taylor, John Deacon & Brian May

♩ = 120

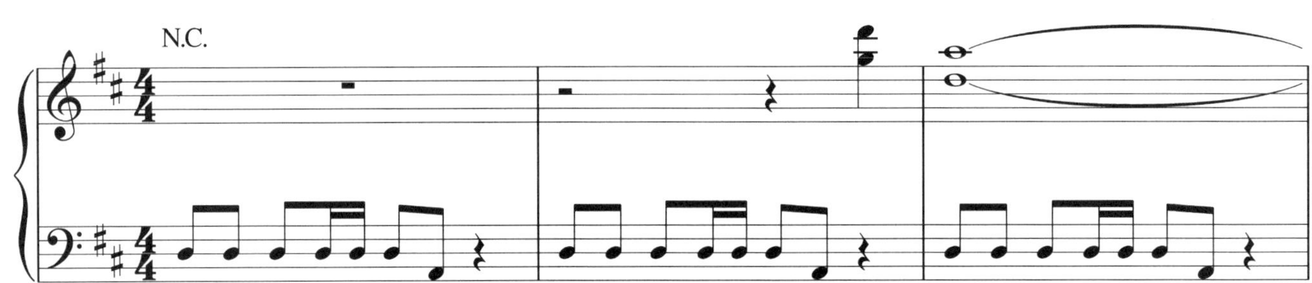

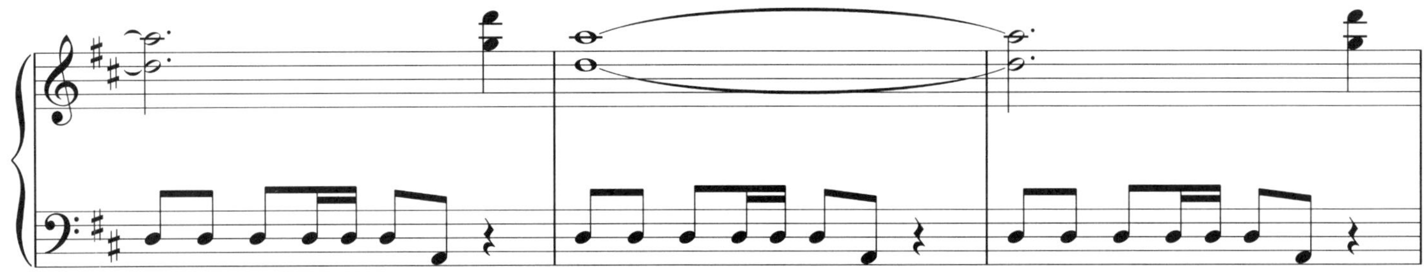

D
A/D
(Both) Pres - sure push - ing down on me,___ press - ing
G/D
A/D
D
down on you___ no man ask for. Un - der pres - sure that burns a
A/C♯
G/B
A
G/A
build - ing down, splits a fam - 'ly in two,_ puts peo - ple on streets.
D
A/C♯
Dsus4/B
Boom bah bah bay, boom bah bah bay, do day dah, do day dah.

A
Gadd9
3fr
That's O. K. (V1) That's the ter - ror of know - ing what this world is a - bout.
A/G
G
Watch - ing some good friends scream - ing "Let me out!" Pray to - mor - row_ takes me
A/G
G
D/F♯
G
A
high - er, pres - sure on peo - ple, peo - ple on streets.
N.C.
D
Do do do. Ba da ba ba ba. O. K._

D
A/D
(V2) Chip - ping a round, kick my brains round the
G/D
A/D
D
floor. These are the days it nev - er rains but it pours. Ee do day doh,
A/C♯
G/B
A
G/A
D
ee da bo ba bop. Mm da bop, bay dop! (V1) Peo pleon streets. (V2) De de
A/C♯
Dsus4/B
A
dee do day. (V1) Peo-ple on streets. (V2) De de dee do dee do dee do. (V1) It's the

Gadd9
3fr
ter - ror of know - ing what this world is a - bout,
A/G
G
watch - ing some good friends scream - ing (Both) "Let me out!" (V2) Pray to - mor - row, take me
A/G
D/F♯
G
A
high high - er.
(V1) Pres - sure on peo - ple, peo - ple on streets.
G
C
(V2)
(V1) Turned a - way from it all like a blind man,

G
C
G
sat on a fence but it don't work. (V1) Keep com - ing up with love but it's so
C
Am
F
slashed and torn, (V2) why? Why, Why?
A
(V1) Love, love, love, love. In -
G
D
-san - i - ty laughs, un - der pres - sure we're crack - ing. (V2) Can't we give our - selves one more

G
A
G
D
G
A
G
chance? Why can't we give love one more chance? Why can't we
D
G
A
G
D
A/C♯
give love, give love, give love, give love, give love, give love, give love, give love.
(Both) 'Cos
G/B
A
D
A/C♯
love's such an old fash - ioned word and love dares you to
Gadd9/B
A
D
A/C♯
Gadd9/B
care for the peo - ple on the edge of the night and love dares you to

A
A7/G
Gsus2
A7/G
Gsus2
A7/G
Gsus2
change our way of car - ing a - bout our - selves this is our
A7/G
Gsus2
D/F♯
G
A
D
last dance. This is our - selves. (V1) Un - der pres - sure.
G/D
A/D
(Both) Un - der pres - sure.
D
G
A
Repeat to fade
(V1) Pres - sure.
Click

Up Where We Belong

Words & Music by Jack Nitzsche, Will Jennings & Buffy Sainte-Marie

Em7
A
D
D/F#
road is long. There are moun-tains in our way,
G
G/B
C
A
G/A
A
but we climb a / climb them a step ev-'ry day.
cresc.
D
D/F#
G
Bm
(Both) Love lift us up where we be-long, where the
f
Em
D/F#
C
G
A
ea-gles cry on a moun-tain high.

D
D/F♯
G
Bm
Love lift us up where we be - long, far from the
Em
D/F♯
1
F♯/A♯
Bm
Gm
3fr
D
G/D
A/D
world we know; (Male) up where we clear winds blow.
3
decresc.
G/D
Gm6/D
2
G/A
A
F
C/E
clear winds blow. Time goes by,
E♭
3fr
B♭/D
D♭
A♭/C
B♭
Fm7/B♭
E♭
3fr
no time to cry, life's you and I, a - live, to - day.

Eb
Eb/G
Ab
Cm
(Both) Love lift us up where we be - long,
where the
Fm
Eb/G
Db
Ab
Bb
ea - gles cry,
on a moun - tain high.
Eb
Eb/G
Ab
Cm
Love lift us up where we be - long
far from the
Repeat ad lib to Fade
Fm
Eb/G
G/B
Cm
Abm
world we know;
where the clear winds blow.

Where The Wild Roses Grow

Words & Music by Nick Cave

Cm
(Am)
Gm
(Em)
F5
(D5)
4º To Coda
know
for my name was E - li - sa
Gm
(Em)
Gm
(Em)
B♭
(G)
Day.
1. From the first day I saw her I knew she was the one as she
(Verses 2 & 3 see block lyric)
Cm
(Am)
D
(B)
Gm
(Em)
stared in my eyes and smiled, for her lips were the col - our of the
B♭
(G)
Cm
(Am)
D
(B)
ro - ses that grew down the ri - ver all blood - y and wild.
(F) When he

Gm
(Em)
B♭
(G)
knocked on my door and en - tered the room, my
Cm
(Am)
D
(B)
trem-bling sub - si - ded in his sure em - brace, he would
Gm
(Em)
B♭
(G)
Cm
(Am)
be my first man and with a care - ful hand, he wiped at the tears that
D
(B)
Play 3 times
D.S.al Coda
ran down my face. (Both) They

Verse 2:

(Male) On the second day I brought her a flower,
She was more beautiful than any woman I've seen.
I said, "Do you know where the wild roses grow
So sweet and scarlet and free?"

(Female) On the second day he came with a single red rose,
He said, "Give me your loss and your sorrow."
I nodded my head, as I lay on the bed,
"If I show you the roses will you follow?"

Verse 3:

(Female) On the third day he took me to the river,
He showed me the roses and we kissed,
And the last thing I heard was a muttered word
As he knelt above me with a rock in his fist.

(Male) On the last day I took her where the wild roses grow
She lay on the bank, the wind light as a thief,
And I kissed her goodbye, said, "All beauty must die"
And I leant down and planted a rose 'tween her teeth.

You're The One That I Want

Words & Music by John Farrar

it's e - lec - tri - fy - in'!
(2.) (Feel your way)
C
Em
(Female) You bet - ter shape up, 'cos I need a man,
Am
F
and my heart is set on you.
C
You bet - ter shape up, you bet - ter un -

Em
Am
-der-stand
to my heart
F
I must be true.
(Male) No-thin' left,
no-thin'
C
left for me to do.
(Female) You're the
one that I want,
F
C
you, oo, oo, hon-ey.
The one that I want,

Verse 2:

(Female) If you're filled with affection you're too shy to convey,
Meditate in my direction, feel your way.

(Male) I better shape up 'cos you need a man,
(Female) I need a man who can keep me satisfied.
(Male) I better shape up if I'm gonna prove,
(Female) You'd better prove that my faith is justified.

(Male) Are you sure?
(Both) Yes, I'm sure down deep inside.

You're the one *etc.*

When You're Gone

Words & Music by Bryan Adams & Eliot Kennedy

C F/C C F/C C Dm
Well, the phone don't ring 'cos my friends
Oh, this is tor-ture, this
G C F/C C
ain't home, I'm tired o' be-in' all a-lone. Got the T.
is pain, it feels like I'm gon-na go in-sane. I hope
Dm B♭
V. on, 'cos the ra-di-o's play-in' songs
you're com-ing back real soon 'cos I don't
G
that re-mind me of you.
know what to do.
Ba-by, when you're

Dm
F
C
G
gone, I real - ise I'm in love.
Dm
F
Days go on an' on, and the nights just seem
C
G
Dm
F
so long. Ev - en food don't taste that good;
C
G
drink ain't do - in' what it should. Things just feel so

Dm
B♭
G
To Coda
wrong,
ba - by, when you're gone.
1.
2.
2. I've been driv -
Dm
G
C
Dm
G
C

Dm G C

Dm B♭

1 2 3 4 5 6 7 8 9